Northeast Scotland

A Landscape Fashioned by Geology

Scottish Natural Heritage
Dualchas Nàdair na h-Alba
All of nature for all of Scotland
Nàdar air fad airson Alba air fad

www.snh.org.uk

© Scottish Natural Heritage 2009

Acknowledgments
Authors: Jon Merritt (British Geological Survey) and Graham Leslie (British Geological Survey)
Series editor: Alan McKirdy (SNH)
Production manager: Pam Malcolm (SNH)
Design and production: SNH Publishing

Photography: Aberdeen Art Gallery & Museums Collections 12 top left, 12 top right, 16 left;
British Geological Survey 12 bottom, 15 right, 26 top, 32 bottom, 32 bottom left, 40 left, 45;
Lorne Gill/SNH front cover, back cover, frontispiece, opposite contents, 4&5, 6, 7 top, 7 bottom, 8, 9,
10&11, 13, 14&15, 16&17, 18 bottom, 19, 20 top, 20&21, 22, 23, 24&25, 26 bottom, 27, 29, 30, 33,
34&35, 37, 38, 39, 40&41, 44, 46 left, 46&47, 48, 49 top & bottom, 50, 51 top, 52&53, 53 right, 54 left
& right, 55, 56, 57, 58&59, 60, 61; **John Gordon** 36 top, 45 left, 45 right; **Pat & Angus Macdonald**
51 bottom; **National Museums of Scotland** 20 bottom, 32 bottom left, 32 bottom right;
SNH/Grampian 18 top, 42&43.

Illustration: Richard Bonson 4 left; **Iain McIntosh** 1; **Craig Ellery** 2, 3, 28, 31, 36;
Clare Hewitt 32 top; **SNH** 18.

ISBN: 978 1 85397 521 9

W2K1009

Further copies are available from: Publications,
Scottish Natural Heritage, Battleby, Redgorton, Perth PH1 3EW
Tel 01738 458530 Fax 01738 456613 pubs@snh.gov.uk

This publication is printed on Revive Pure. This paper is made from 100%
recycled fibre and is fully FSC certified.

Front cover image and
Frontispiece:
Dunnottar Castle, near Stonehaven.
Back cover image:
The village of Pennan, beneath a
cliff of Old Red Sandstone.

Northeast Scotland

A Landscape Fashioned by Geology

by

Jon Merritt & Graham Leslie

1

Contents

1
Floodplain of the River Dee
looking west, near Braemar.

1

Introduction

The area described in this book extends northeast from the Cairngorms, and is bounded by the Moray Firth and the North Sea. It encompasses the heather-clad mountains that provide the backdrop to the beautiful landscape of Royal Deeside and a swath of more remote, rolling hills and glens to the north that include many of the famous whisky distilleries of the region. Buchan is characterised by its quiet, gently undulating farmland and overlooked by Bennachie, a tor-topped mountain of granite entwined in the folklore and Doric poetry of the region. The land terminates abruptly at a coastline of sheer rocky cliffs, steep tumbledown slopes, wide expanses of sand dunes and a variety of beaches. A string of closely crammed fishing villages shelters in rocky coves from the harsh seas.

The overall impression is one of an open, large-scale landscape, with wide vistas of sea and sky merging together at the horizon. It is a unique landscape fashioned over many millions of years by both geological and geomorphological processes.

1
The iconic skyline of Bennachie, viewed southward across the Buchan farmland.

Northeast Scotland Through Time

QUATERNARY
2.6 million years ago to the present day

11, 500 years ago. The climate warmed abruptly and our present 'Interglacial' period began. Dense woodland was present by 8,000 years ago, and sea level peaked at a few metres above present-day levels at about 6,000 years ago.
12, 500 years ago. An Arctic climate returned, corrie glaciers reappeared in the Cairngorms and tundra-like, Siberian conditions gripped the region.
14, 700 years ago. The climate warmed, ice melted quickly and torrents of meltwater released their burdens of sand and gravel as they flowed into seas that were many metres higher than today.
28,000 years ago. A thick ice sheet covered Scotland, extending to the continental shelf margin. Early in the glaciation, Scandinavian ice occupied the North Sea basin, causing the Moray Firth glacier to deflect across Buchan towards Aberdeen.
132,000 years ago. The last 'Interglacial' period began, followed by about 90,000 years of mostly very cold, Arctic tundra conditions.
2.6 million years ago. Climate cooled and the 'Ice Age' began. Numerous very cold episodes were interspersed with shorter, warmer periods. At least two widespread glaciations affected the region.

NEOGENE
23 to 2.6 million years ago

'Topographic inversion' occurred in Buchan as the region was eroded under a subtropical and then temperate climate. Eastward-flowing rivers laid down the Buchan Gravels, reworking residual flint deposits.

PALAEOGENE
65 to 23 million years ago

Volcanoes erupted to the west of Scotland about 60 million years ago as the North Atlantic Ocean began to open. Northeast Scotland was uplifted and tilted to the east in a humid tropical climate.

CRETACEOUS
145 to 65 million years ago

Now around 45 degrees north, warm, shallow seas covered most of Scotland. Rocks of this age are rare on land, but are widespread just offshore.

JURASSIC
200 to 145 million years ago

The Scottish Highlands formed high ground on the margins of shallow seas, and dinosaurs roamed along the coast. Rocks of this age occur beneath the Moray Firth, and are a source of oil in the North Sea basin.

TRIASSIC
251 to 200 million years ago

Seasonal rivers flowed westwards across open plains depositing wide spreads of silts, sands and pebbly gravels. A rich Triassic reptile fauna is preserved at Lossiemouth

PERMIAN
299 to 251 million years ago

Scotland had drifted 10 to 20 degrees north of the equator and was again hot and dry. Desert sands containing reptile fossils are preserved around Hopeman and Elgin.

CARBONIFEROUS
359 to 299 million years ago

Scotland lay close to the equator and parts of the country were covered in tropical forests, from which the coal of central Scotland formed. Dolerite dykes were intruded at the end of the Carboniferous.

DEVONIAN
416 to 359 million years ago

Scotland had become part of a vast, arid continent. Magma continued to accumulate beneath the surface of Northeast Scotland forming dykes and more granites, while sand and muds were deposited by rivers and in lakes in mountainous areas at the surface. Volcanic eruptions and hot spring activity occurred around Rhynie.

SILURIAN
444 to 416 million years ago

Northeast Scotland lay about 15 degrees south of the Equator. It was dry and mountainous, with deep valleys that flooded during rare wet periods. Magma accumulated at depth, and rising, cooled to form granites.

ORDOVICIAN
488 to 444 million years ago

Colliding volcanic arcs and continents formed a chain of mountains on the edge of the old Laurentian continent; the Dalradian sediments were deeply buried, compressed and heated, and deformed into spectacular folds.

CAMBRIAN
542 to 488 million years ago

Sediments, now seen only in the North-west Highlands, continued to be deposited on the flanks of Laurentia, whilst other continental masses moved ever closer together, narrowing the intervening ocean.

PRECAMBRIAN
Before 542 million years ago

The Dalradian sediments were laid down in an expanding Iapetus Ocean on the margins of a continent known as Laurentia.

Brown bars indicate periods of time represented by the rocks and sediments seen across Northeast Scotland.

Geological Map of Northeast Scotland

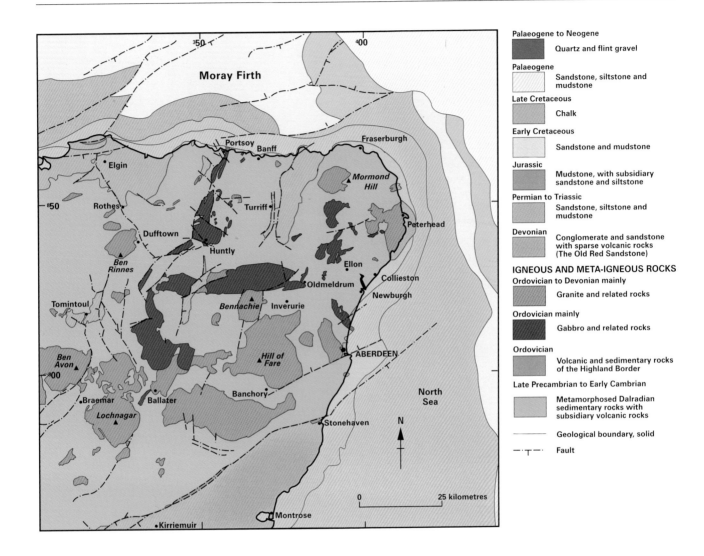

Palaeogene to Neogene
Quartz and flint gravel

Palaeogene
Sandstone, siltstone and mudstone

Late Cretaceous
Chalk

Early Cretaceous
Sandstone and mudstone

Jurassic
Mudstone, with subsidiary sandstone and siltstone

Permian to Triassic
Sandstone, siltstone and mudstone

Devonian
Conglomerate and sandstone with sparse volcanic rocks (The Old Red Sandstone)

IGNEOUS AND META-IGNEOUS ROCKS

Ordovician to Devonian mainly
Granite and related rocks

Ordovician mainly
Gabbro and related rocks

Ordovician
Volcanic and sedimentary rocks of the Highland Border

Late Precambrian to Early Cambrian
Metamorphosed Dalradian sedimentary rocks with subsidiary volcanic rocks

Geological boundary, solid

Fault

3

Ancient Oceans and Continents

About 600 million years ago, Scotland lay in the southern hemisphere, within a huge ancient continent called Rodinia. At about this time, movements of the crustal plates that make up the outer layer of the Earth caused the Earth's crust to become stretched and thinned. That stretching and thinning continued, leading eventually to the rupture and break-up of Rodinia. The continental fragments were pushed farther apart by the creation of a new ocean, which geologists refer to as the Iapetus Ocean. Scotland now lay on the north side of this ocean, on the margin of an ancient landmass called Laurentia, which also included Greenland and Svalbard. A similar process is stretching the crust of northeast Africa and Arabia today, and has created the Red Sea rift between those two regions.

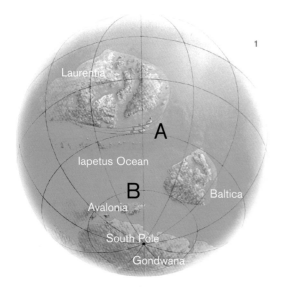

1

1
The globe depicts how a map of the world may have looked 500 million years ago. Scotland (A), located south of Greenland, was a little piece of Laurentia, separated from Avalonia (England and Wales) (B) by the Iapetus Ocean.
2
Sand dunes on the North Sea coast at Forvie National Nature Reserve.

2

3

The Iapetus Ocean existed for some 180–200 million years but then disappeared again as the crustal plates collided back together in a new configuration of continents. That collision ultimately created the Caledonian mountain belt, in an event which geologists call the Caledonian Orogeny. Scotland now preserves only the roots of that ancient mountain belt, which originally is likely to have been comparable in scale to the Himalayas. The rocks of the Caledonian mountain belt in Scotland are similar in many respects to rocks of the same age now preserved from eastern Greenland to the Appalachians, all of which experienced the Caledonian Orogeny.

The metamorphic and igneous rocks that dominate the bedrock geology of Northeast Scotland preserve a record of that Caledonian episode of Earth history. Younger sedimentary rocks deposited on these metamorphic and igneous rocks record the later history of the Caledonian mountain belt, including the start of a long period of erosion which has continued through the recent glacial history of the region until the present day.

3
Metamorphosed Dalradian sandstones form the cliffs at Portnockie, Moray Firth coast.
4
The Maiden Stone, Pittodrie.
5
Devonian sandstones and conglomerates form the North Sea cliffs at Fowlsheugh.

4

5

Ocean Sediments and Mountains

Geologists refer to the oldest rocks which we now see in the northeast of Scotland as the Dalradian. These rocks, which date back to the Precambrian Era, tell us the history of the ancient 'Scottish' margin of the Iapetus Ocean. Layers of sand, mud and limestone accumulated first in relatively shallow, near-shore marine conditions but in time, as the Iapetus Ocean began to develop and the ancient continents moved farther apart, sediments and volcanic deposits accumulated in deeper and deeper water farther from the coastline. Similar sequences of sedimentary and volcanic rocks, developed at the European continental margin of the North Atlantic over the last 60 million years, provide a good indication of the Precambrian rocks that would have formed along the 'Scottish' margin of Laurentia. Most of these Dalradian sediments accumulated at a time before the Cambrian explosion of life on Earth, and so the Dalradian rocks of Northeast Scotland contain no shelly fossils.

1
Flat-lying fold in metamorphosed Dalradian sandstones, Devil's Study, Whinnyfold, North Sea coast.

1

2

As these rocks were compressed and heated during deformation, crystals of new metamorphic minerals grew in the rocks. These crystals were typically aligned parallel to each other, so that the metamorphic rocks we now see at the surface have a marked tendency to split more easily in a single preferred direction. The old slate quarry workings, which are scattered across the Glens of Foudland and westwards towards Rhynie, show where man has exploited this characteristic.

The metamorphic minerals recognised in the rocks of Northeast Scotland are different in detail to those found in the metamorphic rocks of the southern Highlands. Over fifty years ago, the metamorphic rocks of Moray/Buchan were used by the well-known geologist H.H. Read to define the Buchan zones of regional metamorphism. These differed from another set of zones, the Barrovian zones, which had been defined by George Barrow in the Southern Highlands. Both schemes are now recognised as regional variations in the metamorphism which was generated by building the Caledonian mountain belt, and have been applied worldwide in understanding this type of metamorphism.

The Dalradian sediments were all deeply buried, heated and compressed as a consequence of the Caledonian mountain-building event. Soft sediments were converted to sedimentary rock, then further deformed and metamorphosed so that we now find schists and marbles instead of the original sandstones, mudstones and limestones. As the rocks were squeezed between the converging crustal plates, the rock layers were folded and contorted, and often turned upside down. The resulting fold structures can be seen in many places along the Moray Firth coast, such as Portsoy, Kinnaird Head, and Fraserburgh, as well as on the North Sea coast at Collieston.

2
The Needle's Eye near Macduff, Moray Firth coast; an arch eroded in metamorphosed Dalradian sandstones.
3
Slate quarry workings in metamorphosed Dalradian mudstones, Glens of Foundland, Aberdeenshire.

Gabbros and Granites

Metamorphic changes are not the only evidence of the increased temperatures that affected the Dalradian rocks as the Iapetus Ocean was consumed. Large volumes of magma (molten rock) were injected into the deformed and metamorphosed Dalradian strata as the crustal plates collided. The magma cooled and crystallised to form large bodies (plutons) of igneous rock; different types of magma produced different types of igneous rock, such as granite and gabbro. The granites are closely associated with the Dalradian rocks which had experienced the highest temperature metamorphic changes. In such areas, some of the metamorphic rocks were heated to such a degree that they began to melt, producing magma that coalesced into larger bodies and eventually cooled to form granite. Many examples of this transformation process can be seen in the coastal outcrops south of Aberdeen at Cove. The Aberdeen granite, famously quarried at Rubislaw in Aberdeen, is one of the best known of the granite intrusions generated in this way.

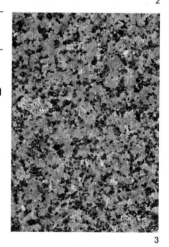

1
Stonemasons carving the Aberdeen War Memorial out of granite blocks, 1924.
2
Rubislaw Quarry, circa 1880.
3
Polished slab of Peterhead granite.
4
Kemnay Quarry today.

6

Gabbro is simply a coarse-grained version of basalt. Whereas basalt is typically found as rapidly cooled lava erupted at the Earth's surface, gabbros form from the same type of magma but cooled more slowly and typically deep below the surface. Gabbro intrusions are widely distributed across Aberdeenshire, and are typically deeply weathered to form relatively low-lying areas and smooth hillsides. The weathering products of the gabbroic rocks very often provide rich soils and a productive agricultural landscape. The gabbros were intruded as magma sufficiently hot to leave an imprint on the surrounding Dalradian rocks so that, for example, many of the slates quarried in the Glens of Foudland are spotted with the growth of a further phase of metamorphic minerals. This process meant that slates close to the gabbro intrusion became thoroughly baked and converted to a hard and splintery rock called hornfels, almost unrecognisable as the original slate and with no tendency to split preferentially in any direction.

Deformation continued after the gabbros were intruded. Differential movement between the rocks now making up Northeast Scotland, and an area of the Grampian Highlands to the west, created a linear zone of crushed and smeared rocks that separated the two blocks of crust. Geologists have named this structure the 'Portsoy Shear Zone'. Gabbroic rocks caught up in this shear zone were intensely deformed while new mineral growth replaced the original crystalline structure of the gabbro; the swirling patterns visible within the transformed rock resulted in the rock name 'serpentinite'. The shear zone, and the serpentinite rocks contained within it, are well displayed on the coast immediately west of Portsoy. It is these serpentinite rocks that provide the source for the popular, and misnamed, 'Portsoy marble'!

5
Looking west along the Moray Firth coast at Portsoy. Steeply dipping rocks in the foreground mark the Portsoy Shear Zone.
6
Portsoy marble.

7

The intrusion of magmas culminated in the late Silurian and early Devonian periods, during the later stages of the Caledonian Orogeny. Numerous large granitic plutons were intruded, along with widespread swarms of thin vertical, sheet-like intrusions (dykes), whilst eruptions of magma at the surface formed volcanic rocks. The granitic intrusions are scattered across the region, from Ben Rinnes in the west to Peterhead in the east, and all along Deeside from Braemar to Hill of Fare. One of the most iconic images of Buchan is the skyline of Bennachie against the lowlands of the Garioch, and the granite tors that form its summit are a magnet for walkers. Bennachie has been identified with Mons Graupius and the battle fought in that region in AD86 at the time of a Roman foray into the region.

The rugged landscape of Royal Deeside owes much to the numerous granitic intrusions located along this major valley. The high plateau rising to the south of the River Dee is dominated by the summits of Lochnagar and Mount Keen, the former immortalised in verse by Lord Byron as 'Dark Lochnagar', and all of these mountain groups represent the eroded tops of large granitic plutons.

The majority of these granite bodies were intruded within a short time interval around 425 million years ago, with each of the plutons being constructed from a series of magma pulses rising up through the crust from a source below. Many of these now show widespread hydrothermal alteration and reddening, later intrusion of very coarse-grained pegmatitic veins, and abundant cavities or vugs, now lined with well-formed crystals, typically quartz. These are all signs which suggest that these plutons were originally

8

formed at relatively shallow levels in the crust, at about 5–8 kilometres below the land surface. However, interpretations of the sub-surface geology, determined from measurements of the Earth's gravitational field, provide compelling evidence that the individual plutons merged at depth to form a huge granite batholith. This would have extended under the Caledonian mountain belt from the present day Monadhliath mountains to Mount Battock.

The granitic bodies became important in the 19th and 20th century economy of the region, when a ring of large quarries developed around Aberdeen. The distinctive red Peterhead granite was one of many exported across the world and can be seen in such famous London buildings as Australia House, Southwark Bridge, the Stock Exchange, the Foreign Office and Covent Garden. Thomas Telford (1757–1834), and many other prominent architects and

engineers of the time were particularly enthusiastic in the use of Peterhead granite, and other examples of buildings built with Peterhead granite may be seen throughout the UK from Aberdeen to Brighton.

7
Marischal College, Aberdeen - one of the largest granite buildings in the world.
8
The distinctive skyline of Bennachie with its granite tors, viewed southward from Old Rayne.

The Old Red Sandstone

During the early part of the Devonian period, the Caledonian mountains were rapidly uplifted and eroded, so that the metamorphic and igneous rocks that had formed in the roots of the mountain belt rose towards the Earth's surface. At that time, the area of the Grampian Highlands must have been one of considerable relief, perhaps resembling the arid mountains of Afghanistan and Pakistan today.

Rivers flowing through the mountains laid down thick deposits of sand and gravel (now known as the Lower Old Red Sandstone) on an eroded surface of Dalradian metamorphic rocks and Caledonian igneous rocks.

Volcanic activity was still ongoing at that time, with granites intruded beneath the surface of the mountain belt while volcanoes erupted at the surface. Volcanic activity is most famously preserved in the Rhynie

Chert, which contains the silicified remains of ancient volcanic springs and of the flora and fauna that survived in these harsh environments. These unique rocks are well protected under the fields around Rhynie.

1
Claw and last segment of a leg of a trigonotarbid (preserved in chert)
2
A model showing the volcanic landscape at the time of formation of the Rhynie Chert, with plant growth around hot springs and pools.
3
Tap o' Noth and the village of Rhynie. The Rhynie Chert lies beneath this farmland.

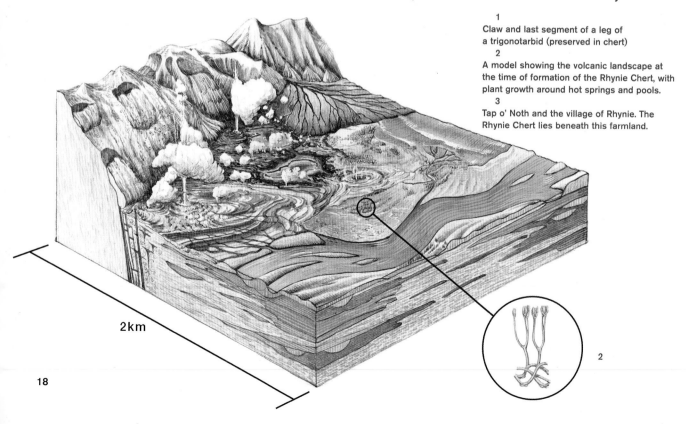

2km

In time the volcanic activity subsided, as did the rates of uplift and erosion, so that the younger deposits of the Middle Old Red Sandstone represent much quieter conditions. These rocks can best be seen along the Moray Firth coast around Gamrie and Pennan, where coarse scree deposits and pebbly rocks called conglomerates are overlain by fine-grained sandstones and limestones that contain fossil fish remains. These Middle Old Red Sandstone rocks accumulated at the southern margin of a large region of interconnected rift valleys and ephemeral lakes referred to collectively as the Orcadian Basin. The remarkably preserved fossil freshwater fish can be traced across this system of ancient lakes, from the outcrops found on the present day Moray Firth coast to the Orkney Islands.

5

4
Old Red Sandstone and conglomerate, Pennan.
5
Fossil fish preserved in a carbonate concretion.
6
The village of Pennan, nestled beneath cliffs formed in Lower Old Red sandstone and conglomerate, Moray Firth coast.

1

The Highland Line

Both of the major boundaries to the Grampian Highlands – the Great Glen Fault to the northwest and the Highland Border to the southeast – are spectacular scenic features. The softer rocks of the Midland Valley of Scotland are separated from the more resistant metamorphic and igneous rocks of the Highlands by a very large fracture called the Highland Boundary Fault. Differential erosion on either side of this fault has left an abrupt hill scarp which can be traced from Loch Lomond in the southwest to Stonehaven in the northeast – this is the 'Highland Line' of history.

The Highland Boundary Fault is recognised as consisting of an interconnected system of fractures and dislocations which have been traced all the way across Scotland from Stonehaven to Arran, affecting a swath of rocks up to 500 metres or so wide. The fault is known to have had a long and complex history of repeated movement. The trace of the fault zone is marked by the presence of fault-bounded slivers of ancient ocean floor rocks of probable Cambrian to Ordovician age, examples of which are well-exposed on the coast at Stonehaven. Volcanic rocks are interlayered with sedimentary rocks in these exposures; the volcanic rocks include pillow lavas, which formed when lava was erupted under water, producing tube- or pillow-shaped bodies such as can be seen today off the coast of Hawaii. These ancient Highland Boundary Fault rocks are thus interpreted as remnants of the Iapetus Ocean consumed during the Caledonian Orogeny.

2

1
Rolling farmland in the Howe of the Mearns, looking northwest across the Highland Boundary Fault.
2
View northeast over Craigeven Bay towards Garron Point.

The type of displacement of the blocks of crust on either side of the fault zone towards the end of the Caledonian Orogeny is uncertain, but most geologists would favour a large degree of sideways (or strike-slip) movement. Subsequent movements of the Highland Boundary Fault during the Devonian and Lower Carboniferous were mainly in a vertical sense, with the Highland block displaced upwards relative to the Midland Valley. Movement had apparently ceased on this important structural line by about 300 million years ago, since thin vertical dykes, formed at the end of the Carboniferous, cross the fault zone with no sign of any significant later displacement.

3
Cowie Bay, near Stonehaven. The Highland Boundary Fault passes just behind the red cliff line. Lower Old Red Sandstone rocks are seen on the shore in the foreground.

3

Glimpses of an Ancient Landscape

Despite mostly being underlain by hard, resistant rocks, the topography of much of Northeast Scotland is surprisingly subdued, comprising rolling hills, gently undulating plateaux and low-lying basins. Unlike most of the country, this part of Scotland was relatively little eroded by glaciers during the Ice Age, and so many elements of the pre-glacial landscape have survived, especially in central Buchan. However, natural exposures and outcrops are sparse, so one has to search diligently for evidence in temporary exposures, quarries and sand pits, spade in hand. Only then is the unique geomorphological record of the region revealed.

1

1
Remnants of a former land surface (a palaeosol) preserved beneath rubbly glacial deposits at Kirkhill Quarry, near Peterhead. The paleosol, black above and white below, formed during a warm, humid interglacial period some 430,000 years ago.
2
Mormond Hill, near Peterhead. The remnant of an ancient inselberg formed of resistant quartzite.
3
Ancient high-level erosion surfaces seen across Glen Clunie, near Braemar. Periglacial stone lobes in the foreground.

2

Erosion surfaces

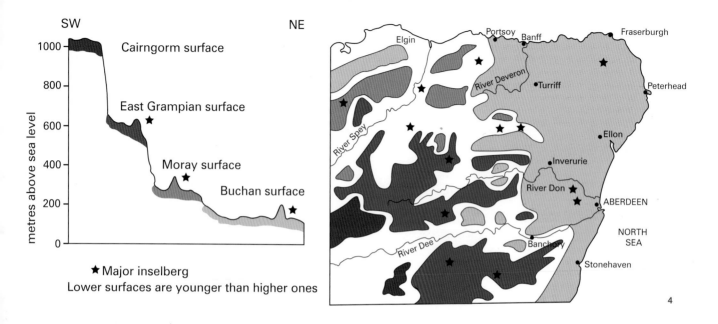

SW — NE

Cairngorm surface
East Grampian surface
Moray surface
Buchan surface

metres above sea level: 1000, 800, 600, 400, 200, 0

★ Major inselberg
Lower surfaces are younger than higher ones

Map labels: Elgin, Portsoy, Banff, Fraserburgh, River Deveron, Turriff, Peterhead, River Spey, Ellon, Inverurie, River Don, ABERDEEN, NORTH SEA, River Dee, Banchory, Stonehaven

In fact, this part of Scotland has been worn down by the elements for a very long time indeed. Some facets of the landscape can be traced back to Devonian times, when the area was essentially a desert, and lay in the Southern Hemisphere. Since then, Northeast Scotland has largely remained above sea level, over a period of nearly 400 million years. Only a few short periods of raised sea level led to the region being submerged; a small outcrop of fossiliferous Lower Cretaceous sandstone at Moreseat, 10 kilometres southeast of Peterhead,

results from one such marine inundation. Across Britain, the most common deposit formed in the shallow Upper Cretaceous seas was chalk – a white limestone containing abundant flints. Although no chalk has survived in Northeast Scotland, the presence of over 25 metres of flint-rich gravel (the Buchan Gravels) beneath the nearby Moss of Cruden strongly suggests that chalk could have formerly covered much of the area. Chalk deposits have been found a short distance offshore, and are very pure, with little intermixed sand. This tells us that, during the

Upper Cretaceous the region had a very low relief, with little sediment being washed down the rivers. Mormond Hill, near Strichen, is an ancient 'inselberg', rather like Ayers Rock in central Australia, formed of particularly resistant and pure quartzite. It probably formed an upstanding hill during the Cretaceous period, before being drowned by the sea in which the chalk was deposited. Several other inselbergs have been identified across the region.

5

The land was subjected to intense humid, subtropical weathering during the Palaeogene period, followed by more temperate conditions following further uplift and a sharp drop in temperature about 10 million years ago. As a result of this subtropical weathering, decomposed rocks are commonly found to depths of over 30 metres in central Buchan. Dalradian schists and slates have become pale yellowish brown, micaceous sand. Granite has become so weakened that it can be dug out locally to provide a valuable resource of 'granite sand' for bedding pipelines, building foundations and laying paving slabs.

4
Diagram showing erosion surfaces in Northeast Scotland.

5
White decomposed granite at Pittodrie Quarry, on the northeastern flank of Bennachie. The vertical banding in the rock has been bent down-slope by movement of the once-solid rock due to freeze-thaw activity.

1

The Buchan Gravels

Much of the present distribution of ancient landscape elements in Buchan has resulted from 'topographic inversion' during the past 55 million years of weathering and erosion. For example, the Buchan Gravels underlying the Moss of Cruden were deposited within an older valley, but now underlie the highest parts of Buchan. The near spherical, impact-pitted, whitened cobbles of flint and quartzite in these distinctive deposits possibly formed on a beach when uplift of the land caused the sea to withdraw in the early Palaeogene. Rivers then redistributed the gravel across the freshly exposed land surface, which was uplifted and tilted eastwards in association with the development of the North Sea. The gravels have been weathered so severely that only the most resistant rock types in them, such as flint and quartzite, remain. They have a matrix of white kaolin formed by the decomposition of feldspar, similar to china clay deposits in Cornwall. Cobbles of totally decomposed granite and schist occur at depth, together with sparse nodular flints showing few signs of abrasion. There are few exposures of these particular gravels, but similar, younger deposits may be examined in small gravel pits at Windyhills, near Fyvie.

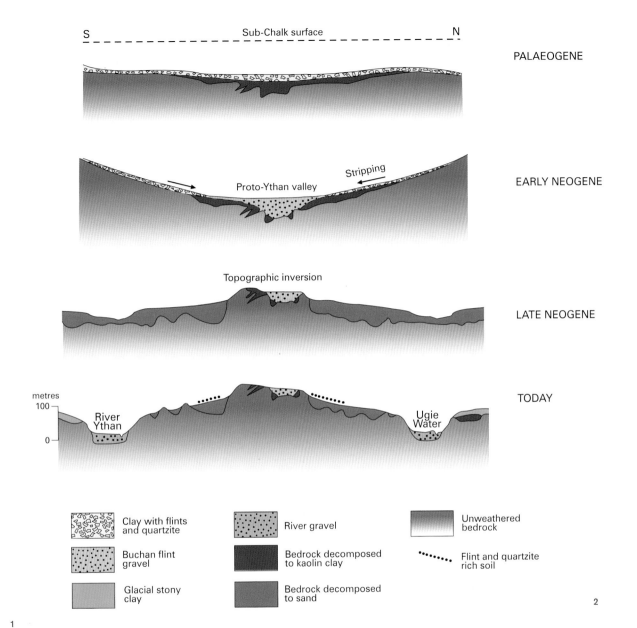

S   Sub-Chalk surface   N

PALAEOGENE

Stripping

Proto-Ythan valley

EARLY NEOGENE

Topographic inversion

LATE NEOGENE

TODAY

metres
100

River
Ythan

Ugie
Water

0

Clay with flints
and quartzite

Buchan flint
gravel

Glacial stony
clay

River gravel

Bedrock decomposed
to kaolin clay

Bedrock decomposed
to sand

Unweathered
bedrock

Flint and quartzite
rich soil

2

1
The Buchan Gravels at Windy Hills, near Fyvie,
deposited by the predecessor of the River Ythan
during the late Neogene.

2
Diagram depicting 65 million years of landscape
evolution, in which the Buchan flint gravel, originally
deposited in a valley, now underlies the highest
ground in central Buchan.

Lack of exposure did not hamper Neolithic people from gathering flints from the Buchan Gravels to make implements such as arrowheads and scrapers. The flints were extracted on a semi-industrial scale! This industry was centred on Den of Boddam, a former glacial drainage channel that cuts through the gravels east of Peterhead. The sides of the channel are pock-marked by numerous round hollows, each one representing the site of a deep bell-pit from which the flints were extracted. Den of Boddam is the only location in Scotland where evidence for prehistoric flint extraction survives on the surface in this way, and the site is of such outstanding importance that it is a Scheduled Ancient Monument.

3
Reconstruction of man mining flints 4,000 years ago at the Den of Boddam.
4
Cobble of flint recovered from the Buchan Gravels underlying the Moss of Cruden.
5
Macehead found at Boddam.
6
Den of Boddam.

The Glacial Legacy of the Lowlands 1

Around 2.6 million years ago, the global climate cooled significantly and the Ice Age began. Since then, very cold glacial periods have been interspersed with short, warmer periods. During the cold periods, ice sheets covered much of the country. These ice sheets extended across Northeast Scotland on several occasions, but the ice in this area was generally very cold and sluggish, being distant from the ice accumulation centres in the Cairngorms and western Highlands.

The ice laid down smooth, very gently undulating sheets of rubbly glacial material called 'till' across Buchan, interspersed with more hummocky spreads of gravelly 'outwash'. These deposits are mainly restricted to the coastal lowlands and to valleys in the more mountainous hinterland, where three contrasting suites occur.

Along the coast northeast of Aberdeen, the soils are a vivid reddish brown in colour. This is because ice last flowed onshore here, carrying within it red-coloured sediments that had been eroded from the seabed. This red suite of deposits extends northwards to Sandford Bay, where it can be examined in the cliffs. Silts and clays capping the sequence were formerly dug for making bricks, both here and at several sites farther down the coast towards Aberdeen. These deposits periodically yielded the bones of whales, seals and birds, suggesting that the retreating ice sheet terminated in the sea, when sea-level was about 30 metres above its present day level. As the ice receded southwards, a meltwater stream flowing towards its margin laid down sand and gravel within an ice-walled tunnel. When the supporting ice melted, it left behind an esker - a sinuous gravel ridge called the Kippet Hills, near Slains. The gravel contains numerous shell fragments and Permian limestone derived from offshore to the southeast.

1
Farmland near Huntly.

From Peterhead northwards towards Fraserburgh, the glacial deposits are bluish grey in colour when freshly exposed. This blue-grey suite of deposits extends sporadically along the coast towards Inverness and was laid down by a huge glacier that flowed out of the Moray Firth. At an early stage in the last glaciation, the glacier ripped up large masses of calcareous, glaciomarine sediment and underlying rocks from the seabed and then deposited them onshore as 'glacial rafts'. Many of these exotic masses of rock or sediment have been found in excavations across Banff and Buchan east of a line between Elgin, Turriff and Aberdeen. The rafts include black mudstones containing ammonites, fossilised wood, white sand and hard, shelly 'greensand'. Until recently a very large raft of mudstone supported an entire brickworks at Whitehills, near Banff.

2

Bluish grey deposits from the Moray Firth (an earlier flow carried glacial rafts towards Aberdeen)

Fraserburgh

Banff

Peterhead

Turriff

Ellon

Yellowish brown deposits from inland and the west

Inverurie

Vivid reddish brown deposits from offshore

ABERDEEN

Banchory

Stonehaven

Reddish brown deposits from Strathmore

0   25 kilometres

Montrose

3

2
A modern-day glacier in Iceland.
3
Diagram showing former directions of ice flow.
4
The Kippet Hills and Meikle Loch, Slains.

The Glacial Legacy of the Lowlands 2

For a long time it has been a puzzle why the Moray Firth glacier over-rode Buchan instead of simply flowing out to sea. Similarly, why did ice from the North Sea flow onshore to lay down the red suite of deposits north of Aberdeen? Many have suggested that ice crossed the North Sea from Scandinavia, blocking the outward flow of Scottish ice. This has been confirmed recently by offshore geophysical seismic and echo-sounding surveys that reveal glacial gouges that can be traced towards the Baltic Sea. Furthermore, pebbles of Norwegian origin have been found in glacial deposits towards the foot of the cliffs at Sandford Bay.

1
A massive stone wall near Ythanbank in the Ythan Valley where boulder-strewn glacial deposits have been cleared to create farmland.

2
Glacial resculpturing of Old Red Sandstone bedrock near Findon.

3

There has been fierce debate as to whether the most recent ice sheet reached out to central Buchan from the Highlands. This is mainly because the glacial deposits there are thin and patchy, and they appear to be weathered. However, this yellow-brown, very sandy suite of deposits looks old because it was largely derived from decomposed bedrock when ice flowed eastwards across the area. Large pebbles are common, many derived from kernels of relatively fresh rock ('corestones') that formerly occurred within partially decomposed granitic and gabbroic rocks. Proof that Buchan experienced the most recent glaciation comes from the presence of numerous winding channels that criss-cross the area. Known locally as 'dens' or 'slacks', these channels formerly carried meltwater, which flowed at the ice margin as the ice retreated slowly westwards across the area.

A good example of such a channel is the Den of Boddam, which formerly carried meltwater northwards across the watershed. Another series of channels carried meltwater 10 kilometres from the vicinity of Hatton, via the Laeca Burn, over the watershed into West Dens and then into the valley of the River Ugie. The Ythan Gorge, upstream of Methlick, also carried glacial meltwater. Although the River Ythan now flows towards the North Sea, during the latter part of the last glaciation it flowed in the opposite direction. The mouth of the valley was blocked by ice at the coast after the headwaters had become ice free, so water became ponded in the lower reaches of the valley, then spilled out via the gorge. The water flowed towards Turriff via a shallow 'glacial spillway' followed by the A947 road and thence towards the Moray Firth down the valley of the River Deveron.

3
A pebble of distinctive Norwegian rock from near Oslo, found in glacial deposits at Sandford Bay, south of Peterhead.
4
The River Ythan upstream of Methlick where it flows through a shallow gorge cut originally by glacial meltwaters.

4

40

1

The Siberian Record

Although the past two and a half million years have witnessed the repeated growth of glaciers in Scotland, for a large part of that time most of the country was not buried beneath ice. In fact even during the relatively short periods of ice-sheet growth most of the snow fell in the mountains of the west, leaving Northeast Scotland as a barren, dry, frozen desert. It was a tundra environment similar to much of modern-day Siberia, and parts of Canada and northern Iceland.

The processes that operated in this frozen environment are referred to as 'periglacial'. They have left an indelible record on the landscape, particularly the smoothing effect that they had on the topography. Repeated freezing and thawing shattered most exposed rock outcrops, reducing them to rubble. Although most of the ground was frozen to many metres, the surface layers would have thawed each summer.

1

The 'Red Rock Hills', near Insch, formed of gabbroic rocks. The subdued, gentle concave slopes illustrated here are typical of landscapes modified during long periods of severe periglacial conditions.

Unable to drain effectively, these wet, gelatinous sediments crept down-slope, rather like porridge, filling in hollows and irregularities in the ground surface. The redistributed materials spread out to form broad, gently concave terraces on the valley floors. Cobbles and boulders migrated to the surface just as stones tend to do in our gardens during frosty winters. Loose sand and silt were picked up by the wind to create ferocious dust storms.

Vertical shrinkage cracks are also quite common in the periglacial sediments, some clearly tapering downwards. The latter phenomena were formed by the growth of

'ground ice' within the permafrost. Modern examples of such ice wedges in arctic Canada have taken many decades to form. Ice wedges and cracks form polygonal networks when viewed from above, like mud cracks. Traces of them can still be observed occasionally in Northeast Scotland, perhaps in low-angle sunlight or in the patterning seen when cereal crops get scorched in dry seasons. The Ugie valley is particularly well known for its fossil tundra polygons.

Granite tors such as those of Bennachie were also mainly created by periglacial processes. Like other rocks in the region, the granite of

Bennachie was weakened by chemical weathering long before the beginning of the Ice Age, especially along the natural vertical and horizontal cracks in the rock mass. Weak material was then removed by periglacial processes, which have revealed these characteristic bastions of granite. Like the tors of the eastern Cairngorms, those on Bennachie and Ben Rinnes appear to have survived several glaciations because they were protected beneath very cold, inactive ice.

2
Bouldery scree at the foot of a granite tor, on Bennachie, formed mainly in a previous periglacial environment.
3
A modern windswept periglacial desert at Hrossaborg in northern Iceland.

The Glacial Legacy of the Upland Valley

Unlike the cold, sluggish ice that covered the low-lying parts of the region during the last glaciation, the ice that flowed down many of the upland valleys was far more vigorous. It scoured away most of the weathered mantle of rock, leaving behind knobs of hard, resistant rock amongst a plethora of bouldery ridges and hummocks of sand and gravel. This diversity of soils and landforms has contributed immensely to the richness of the landscape exemplified in Royal Deeside. Here the beauty created by the yellow and golden hues of the birch and larch in the autumn can be breathtaking, so too the numerous ancient Scots pines set against distant purple, heather-clad hillsides. The cobbles and boulders that form the riverbeds are mostly derived from glacial deposits, providing spawning grounds that help make these rivers some of the best in the world for salmon and trout.

1
The River Dee, near Braemar.
2
View west over Aberarder near Inver, upper Deeside, with U-shaped glaciated valley in the middle distance.

3
Ailnack Gorge near Tomintoul.
4
Burn of Vat, an incised gorge near Ballater.
5
View over Loch Kinord from the viewpoint at Muir of Dinnet National Nature Reserve.

The thin, bouldery and sandy soils bequeathed by the glaciers has made arable farming difficult in these upland valleys, but they were ideally suited for the famous shooting estates of the region that were created in the late eighteenth and nineteenth centuries. The river terraces that border the floodplains have provided the most fertile farmland. They are underlain by sand and cobble gravel deposited by fast-flowing, milky meltwaters that emanated from retreating glaciers. The terraces were subsequently dissected by the rivers, in response to the land surface rebounding as the immense load placed upon it by the ice was removed. The floodplains are underlain by peaty loam that commonly rests on many metres of gravel from which groundwater is abstracted locally.

For example, most of the drinking water in Aberdeen is piped from gravels within the Dee valley upstream.

Landforms formed by glacial meltwaters are particularly widespread in the vicinity of Dinnet, Aboyne and Strachan. In this area, networks of gravelly ridges (eskers) wind around rounded hillocks (kames) and oddly shaped hollows (kettleholes), the latter formed by the melting of masses of ice that had become buried within the glacial outwash deposits. Some cross-valley ridges were formed by the bulldozing action of local glacial readvances. Much of this hummocky, gravelly land has not been cultivated heavily and now supports a rich diversity of herbs, birds, insects and small mammals.

49

The Northern Coastline

The coast of Northeast Scotland is diverse and contains some stunning scenery. The characteristics of the clifflines are mainly determined by the structure, composition and hardness of the rocks that form them. The nature of the beaches depends more upon local sediment sources and the aspect relative to tides, waves and prevailing winds. For example, the steeply shelving shingle beach of Spey Bay is subject to westerly, wave-induced longshore drift that has created a hook-shaped shingle spit at the mouth of the Spey, diverting it westwards. The modern beach is backed by a two kilometres-wide belt of lichen-covered ridges, composed of well rounded, near spherical pebbles. This 'raised beach' was formed some 6,000 years ago, during a period of higher sea level.

1

The Holocene raised beaches backing Spey Bay, and others occurring within inlets close to Troup Head, all tilt gently eastwards. The tilting has occurred because the land has continued to rebound from the enormous weight of ice that covered it some 15,000 years ago. The uplift is centred in the western Highlands, where the ice was thickest. Remnants of an older, higher, more tilted and fragmented set of raised beaches and associated coastal rock platforms may be found; these were formed during and following the retreat of ice from the region.

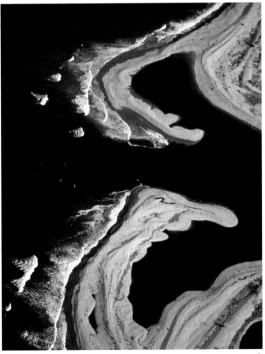

1
The Bow, Portnockie.
2
Rocky coastline near Macduff.
3
The hook-shaped shingle spit at Spey Bay.

3

The shingle beaches give way eastwards to long stretches of high, rugged cliffs along the Banffshire coast, within which a string of little fishing villages nestle within natural havens. The cliffs are broken here and there by deep, secret ravines doubtless exploited by smugglers of old. One such feature of canyon proportions is the infrequently visited Tore of Troup, which is deeply incised into Devonian conglomerates to the south of Pennan. Towards Rattray Head the cliffs yield to huge expanses of golden sand backed by marram-covered dunes and shingle ridges. Some of the storm beach ridges have formed in historical times, because here, unlike in Spey Bay, sea level has continued to rise until the present day. Furthermore, the northward, wave-induced longshore drift has deposited shingle that now separates the Loch of Strathbeg (formerly a tidal lagoon) and the historical port of Old Rattray from the sea.

4
The cliff-backed village of Crovie.
5
The Tore of Troup, a ravine cut mainly by glacial meltwaters.

The Eastern Coastline

Heading southwards, the cliffs return with a vengeance at Boddam Ness, where the sea has gnawed into the pink Peterhead granite to create a ragged coastline. Highly sculpted and fractured cliffs, sea stacks, and treacherous reefs occur here along with other dramatic phenomena such as the Bullers of Buchan blowhole. Generations of convicts have also quarried away granite from the cliffs near Boddam. The next short breach in the high cliffline to the south is the delightful, dune-backed Bay of Cruden, which lies above a buried, sediment-filled valley that may once have been the mouth of the River Ythan before the last glaciation.

1

1
Blowhole, Bullers of Buchan.
2
Sand dunes at Balmedie beach.
3
Rocky coastline at Bullers of Buchan in jointed Peterhead Granite.

2

The spectacular dunes of the Sands of Forvie National Nature Reserve strive to obscure the modern mouth of the River Ythan and its tranquil, mud-dominated estuary that is famous for its flocks of visiting wading birds. A broad sandy beach extends southwards to Aberdeen, fringed by a belt of dunes that have spawned several natural links golf courses. A high cliffline stretches southwards from Aberdeen, broken only by a string of small inlets and bays backed by arcuate beaches of shingle. The towering cliffs of Devonian conglomerate and sandstone at Dunnottar Castle, south of Stonehaven, are certainly worth a visit, so too the idyllic, isolated haven at Catterline with its crescent-shaped shingle beach.

Stonehaven is built on a raised beach that was created shortly after the glaciers retreated. Another underlies the belt of sand dunes to the north of Aberdeen, which also conceals a low, fossil cliffline cut mainly into glacial deposits. These late-glacial raised beaches slope gently to the northeast and the equivalent features lie just below present sea level at Rattray Head.

4
The Sands of Forvie National Nature Reserve at the mouth of the River Ythan.
5
Dunnottar Castle, near Stonehaven, built on cliffs of Devonian conglomerate.

4

5

Cultural Landscape

The coastal communities of Northeast Scotland have grown up over the centuries around the fishing and boat-building industries, whereas inland employment has centred on farming, weaving, lacemaking, quarrying, forestry, whisky distilling and the shooting estates. Beef production was once prevalent, but arable farming has become increasingly important following the application of modern methods of land drainage to the notoriously poorly drained and stony soils of the region. Indeed, Buchan now resembles parts of East Anglia, following the widespread removal of boulders and stone walls. The numerous stone-built dwellings across the region, particularly in the 'Granite City', are lasting monuments to the formerly important stone quarrying industry of the region, which has now been replaced by the production of aggregates and concrete products. Blanket peat is still exploited commercially, as around Strichen, but the many former brick and tile works that exploited glacial clays around the coasts have closed. Tourism, angling, shooting and recreation are now becoming increasingly important.

1
Grouse moors, Corgarff.   1

2

Without doubt, the North Sea oil- and gas-related industries are the mainstays of the present economy of the region, but they have accelerated irrevocable demographic and other changes. This is especially so around Aberdeen and Peterhead where there has been a significant increase in population during the past thirty years. This has led to pressures to release land for building, quarrying and landfill, and a dramatic increase in commuting across the entire region placing pressure on the infrastructure and the landscape.

Human activity has superimposed a distinctive veneer of farmland, woods, moors and settlement on the natural landscape of the region. This character has been created over some 8,000 years by a combination of natural forces and human activities. The land has been exploited and managed in one form or another, from the heather-clad mountaintops to the cliff-edged headlands and dune-fringed coastal plains. Social, political and religious upheavals have resulted in changing patterns of land ownership and land use, producing new landscape

features that we now accept as characteristic of the region, like the numerous 'planned settlements' with their rectilinear layout of streets that arrived in the late eighteenth century. Our capacity to control and develop the land has now reached new heights, accelerating the pace of landscape change.

2
Wind turbine and power lines near Huntly,
3
Peterhead harbour.

3

Scottish Natural Heritage and the British Geological Survey

Scottish Natural Heritage is a government body. Its aim is to help people enjoy Scotland's natural heritage responsibly, understand it more fully and use it wisely so it can be sustained for future generations.

Scottish Natural Heritage
Great Glen House, Leachkin Road,
Inverness IV3 8NW
t: 01463 725000
e: enquiries@snh.gov.uk

Scottish Natural Heritage
Dualchas Nàdair na h-Alba
All of nature for all of Scotland
Nàdar air fad airson Alba air fad

The British Geological Survey maintains up-to-date knowledge of the geology of the UK and its continental shelf. It carries out surveys and geological research.

The Scottish Office of BGS is sited in Edinburgh. The office runs an advisory and information service, a geological library and a well-stocked geological bookshop.

British Geological Survey
Murchison House
West Mains Road
Edinburgh EH9 3LA

British
Geological Survey
NATURAL ENVIRONMENT RESEARCH COUNCIL

Also in the Landscape Fashioned by Geology series...

Arran and the Clyde Islands
David McAdam & Steve Robertson
ISBN 1 85397 287 8
Pbk 24pp £3.00

Ben Nevis and Glencoe
Kathryn Goodenough & David Stephenson
ISBN 1 85397 506 6
Pbk 44pp £4.95

Cairngorms
John Gordon, Rachel Wignall, Ness Brazier,
& Patricia Bruneau
ISBN 1 85397 455 2
Pbk 52pp £4.95

East Lothian and the Borders
David McAdam & Phil Stone
ISBN 1 85397 242 8
Pbk 26pp £3.00

Edinburgh and West Lothian
David McAdam
ISBN 1 85397 327 0
Pbk 44pp £4.95

Fife and Tayside
Mike Browne, Alan McKirdy & David McAdam
ISBN 1 85397 110 3
Pbk 36pp £3.95

Glasgow and Ayrshire
Colin MacFadyen & John Gordon
ISBN 1 85397 451 X
Pbk 52pp £4.95

Glen Roy
Douglas Peacock, John Gordon & Frank May
ISBN 1 85397 360 2
Pbk 36pp £4.95

Loch Lomond to Stirling
Mike Browne & John Mendum
ISBN 1 85397 119 7
Pbk 26pp £2.00

The Glacial Legacy of the Upland Valley

Mull and Iona
David Stephenson
ISBN 1 85397 423 4
Pbk 44pp £4.95

Northwest Highlands
John Mendum, Jon Merritt & Alan McKirdy
ISBN 1 85397 139 1
Pbk 52pp £6.95

Orkney and Shetland
Clive Auton, Terry Fletcher & David Gould
ISBN 1 85397 220 7
Pbk 24pp £2.50

The Outer Hebrides
Kathryn Goodenough & Jon Merritt
ISBN 1 978185397 507 3
Pbk 44pp £4.95

Rum and the Small Isles
Kathryn Goodenough & Tom Bradwell
ISBN 1 85397 370 2
Pbk 48pp £5.95

Scotland: the creation of its natural landscape
Alan McKirdy & Roger Crofts
ISBN 1 85397 004 2
Pbk 64pp £7.50

Skye
David Stephenson & Jon Merritt
ISBN 1 85397 026 3
Pbk 24pp £3.95

Southwest Scotland
Andrew McMillan & Phil Stone
ISBN 978 1 85397 520 2
Pbk 48pp £4.95

Series Editor: Alan McKirdy (SNH)
Other books soon to be produced in the
series include: Argyll & the Islands,
Moray & Caithness

To order these and other publications, visit: www.snh.org.uk/pubs